THE MOVIE SOUNDTRACK FEATURING THE SONGS OF ABBA®

Published by

Wise Publications
14-15 Berners Street, London W1T 3LJ, UK

Exclusive Distributors:

Music Sales Limited
Distribution Centre, Newmarket Road,
Bury St Edmunds, Suffolk IP33 3YB, UK

Music Sales Pty Limited
20 Resolution Drive,
Caringbah, NSW 2229, Australia

Order No. AM997161
ISBN 978-1-84938-029-4

Printed in the EU

www.musicsales.com

Your Guarantee of Quality
As publishers, we strive to produce every book to the highest commercial standards.
The music has been freshly engraved and the book has been carefully designed to minimise awkward page turns and to make playing from it a real pleasure.
Particular care has been given to specifying acid-free, neutral-sized paper made from pulps which have not been elemental chlorine bleached. This pulp is from farmed sustainable forests and was produced with special regard for the environment.
Throughout, the printing and binding have been planned to ensure a sturdy, attractive publication which should give years of enjoyment.
If your copy fails to meet our high standards, please inform us and we will gladly replace it.

Wise Publications
part of The Music Sales Group
London / New York / Paris / Sydney / Copenhagen / Berlin / Madrid / Tokyo

HONEY, HONEY

Words and Music by BENNY ANDERSSON,
BJÖRN ULVAEUS and STIG ANDERSON

Dm
F
Dm
I want-ed to know some more. And
the way that you hold me tight, I
but I know just how you are. And,
F
Dm
B♭
now I know what they mean, you're a love ma-chine.
feel like I wan-na sing when you do your thing, yeah.
hon-ey, to say the least, you're a dog-gone beast, yeah.
1
C7
2, 3
C7sus
C7
Cm7
3fr
Oh, you make me diz-zy. I don't wan-na hurt you, ba-
F7
B♭
Dm7/A
Gm
3fr
Cm7
3fr
-by, I don't wan-na see you cry. So stay on the ground, girl, you

F7
B♭
Fm7
bet-ter not get too high.
But I'm gon-na stick to you,
B♭
E♭
Gm7/D
A♭
boy, you'll nev-er get rid of me.
There's no oth-er place in this
D♭
Gm7sus
C7
D.S.
(take 2nd ending)
world where I rath - er would be.
F
B♭
Hon-ey, hon-ey, how you thrill me, a - ha, hon-ey, hon-ey.
Hon-ey, hon-ey, let me feel it, a - ha, hon-ey, hon-ey.

F
B♭
Hon-ey, hon-ey, near - ly kill __ me, a - ha, hon-ey, hon-ey.
Hon-ey, hon-ey, don't __ con - ceal __ it, a - ha, hon-ey, hon-ey.
F
Dm
I'd heard a - bout you __ be - fore, ______ I
The way that you kiss __ good - night, ______ the
F
Dm
F
want - ed to know __ some more. ______ And now I know what __ they mean, __
way that you hold __ me tight, ______ I feel like I wan - na sing, __
Repeat and Fade
Dm
B♭
C7
__ you're a love ma - chine. __
__ when you do your thing, ____ yeah.
Oh, you make me diz - zy.

MONEY, MONEY, MONEY

Words and Music by BENNY ANDERSSON
and BJÖRN ULVAEUS

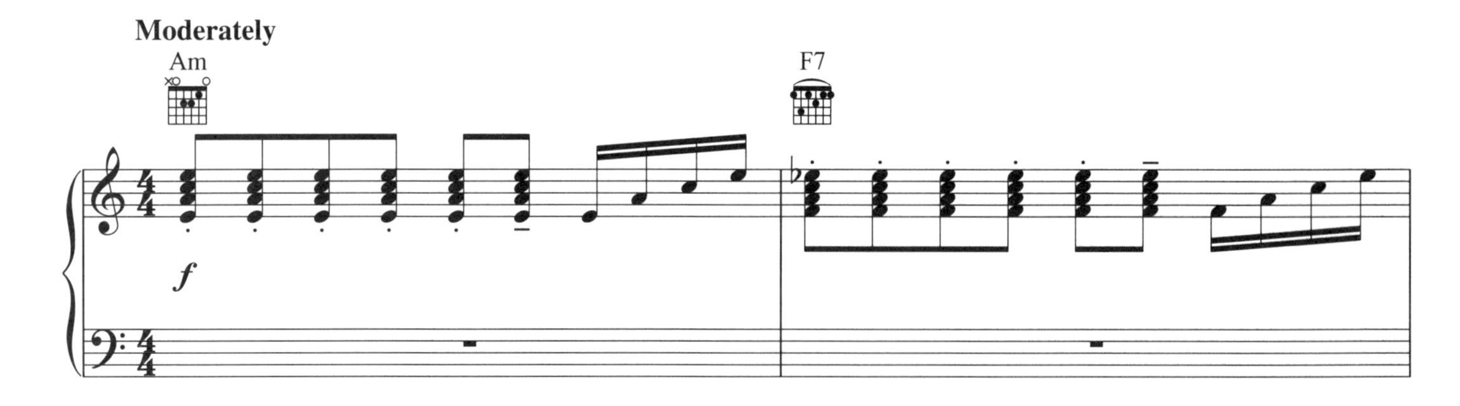

E7
Am
N.C.
Ain't it sad,
and still there nev-er seems to be a
E/G♯
E7♭9
Am
N.C.
sin-gle pen-ny left for me,
that's too bad.
E/A
Am
B♭/F
F
In my dreams I have a plan,
if I got me a
Dm
D♯dim
6fr
wealth-y man
I would-n't have to work at all, I'd fool a-round and have a ball.
dim.
rall.

E7
N.C.
f a tempo

Am
B7
E7
Am
Mon - ey, mon - ey, mon - ey must be fun - ny in a rich man's world. _

B7
Mon - ey, mon - ey, mon - ey al - ways sun - ny

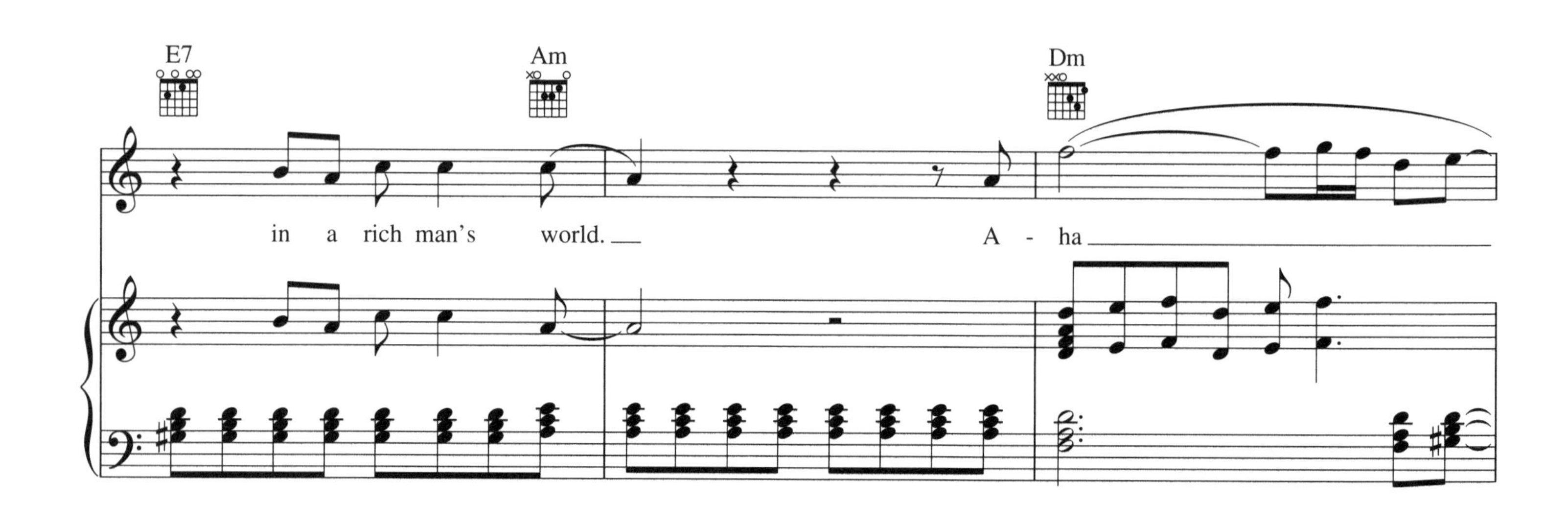
E7
Am
Dm
in a rich man's world. _ A - ha

E7
A
Dm
F7
E7
all the things I could do
if I
Am
Dm
E7♯5
Am
had a lit - tle mon - ey.
It's a rich man's world.
F7
Dm
E7♯5
Am
It's a rich man's world.
mp
E/G♯
A man like that is hard to find, but I can't get him off my mind.

N.C.
E7
Am
Ain't it sad.
And if he hap-pens to be free, I
E/G♯
N.C.
E7♭9
Am
bet he would-n't fan-cy me,
that's too bad.
E/A
Am
B♭/F
F
I must leave,
I'll have to go
to Las Ve-gas or
Dm
D♯dim
6fr
Mo-na-co,
and win a for-tune in a game. My
life would nev-er be the same.
poco rall.

N.C.
Am
Mon - ey, mon - ey, mon - ey
f a tempo
B7
E7
Am
must be fun - ny
in a rich man's world.
B7
E7
Am
Mon - ey, mon - ey, mon - ey
al - ways sun - ny
in a rich man's world.
Dm
E7
A - ha,

A
Dm
F7
E7
Am
all the things I could do
if I had a lit - tle mon - ey.
Dm
E7♯5
Am
F7
It's a rich man's world.
B♭m
C7
F7
B♭m
Mon - ey, mon - ey, mon - ey
must be fun - ny
in a rich man's world.
C7
Mon - ey, mon - ey, mon - ey
al - ways sun - ny

F7
B♭m
E♭m
6fr
in a rich man's world.
A - ha
F7
B♭7
E♭m
G♭7
F7
all the things I could do
if I
B♭m
E♭m
F7♯5
B♭m
had a lit - tle mon - ey,
it's a rich man's world.
G♭7
E♭m
F7♯5
B♭m
It's a rich man's world.

MAMMA MIA

Words and Music by BENNY ANDERSON,
BJÖRN ULVAEUS and STIG ANDERSON

G
D
Look at me now,
D+
D
D+
will I ev - er learn? I don't know how,
but I sud - den - ly lose
G
A
con - trol.
There's a fire with - in my soul.
G D A
G D
Just one look and I can hear a bell ring.
One more

A
look and I for - get ev - 'ry - thing,
oh, oh.
D
Mam - ma Mi - a,
here I go a - gain.
G C/G G D/G D
My, my how can I re - sist ya?
G C/G G
Mam - ma Mi - a,
does it show a - gain,
my, my, just

D/G
D
A/C♯
how much I've missed ya?
Yes, I've been bro - ken - heart - ed,
Bm
A6
G
C
G
Em7
blue since the day we part - ed.
Why, why did
A
D
Bm
To Coda
I ev - er let you go?
Mam-ma Mi - a,
now I real - ly know,
G
C
G
Em7
1
A
D+
my, my, I should not have let you go.

D
D+
2
A
D
D+
should not have let you go.
DONNA: What the hell are you all doing here?
D
D+
Well, I'd love to stop and chat, but I have to go and clean out my handbag or something.
G
Gmaj7
BILL: Age does not wither her.
HARRY: I was expecting a rather stout matron.

A6
A
G
D
SAM: No, she's still Donna.
Just one
A
G
D
look and I can hear a bell ring.
One more
A
D.S. al Coda
look and I for - get ev - 'ry - thing,
oh, oh.
CODA
G
C
G
Em7
A
D
my, my, I should not have let you go.

DANCING QUEEN

Words and Music by BENNY ANDERSSON,
BJÖRN ULVAEUS and STIG ANDERSON

Bm7
E7/B
A
D/A
Watch that scene, diggin' the dancing queen.
A
D/A
A
D/A
A
D/A
Fri - day night and the lights are low.
A
F♯m
Look-ing out for a place to go,
oh,
E
A/E
E
A/E
E
F♯m
where they play the right mu-sic.
Get-ting in the swing,
you come to look for a king.

E
F♯m
A
D/A
An - y - bod - y could be that guy.
You're a teas - er. You turn 'em on,
A
F♯m
E
A/E
Night is young and the mu - sic's high.
leave 'em burn - ing and then you're gone,
With a bit of rock mu - sic,
look - ing out for an - oth - er.
E
A/E
E
F♯m
E
F♯m
ev - 'ry - thing is fine.
An - y - one will do.
You're in the mood for a dance,
and when you
Bm7
E7
A
get the chance,
you are the danc - ing queen,

D/A
A
D/A
young and sweet, only seventeen.
A
D/A
A
E/G♯
Dancing queen, feel the beat from the tambourine.
F♯m7
A/E
E
C♯7
You can dance. You can jive,
F♯m
B7/D♯
D
having the time of your life. Oh, see that girl.

Bm7
E7/B
A
Watch that scene, dig - gin' the danc - ing queen.
D/A
A
1
D/A
A
D/A
A
D/A
2
D/A
Dig - gin' the
A
D/A
A
Repeat and Fade
danc - ing queen.

LAY ALL YOUR LOVE ON ME

Words and Music by BENNY ANDERSSON
and BJÖRN ULVAEUS

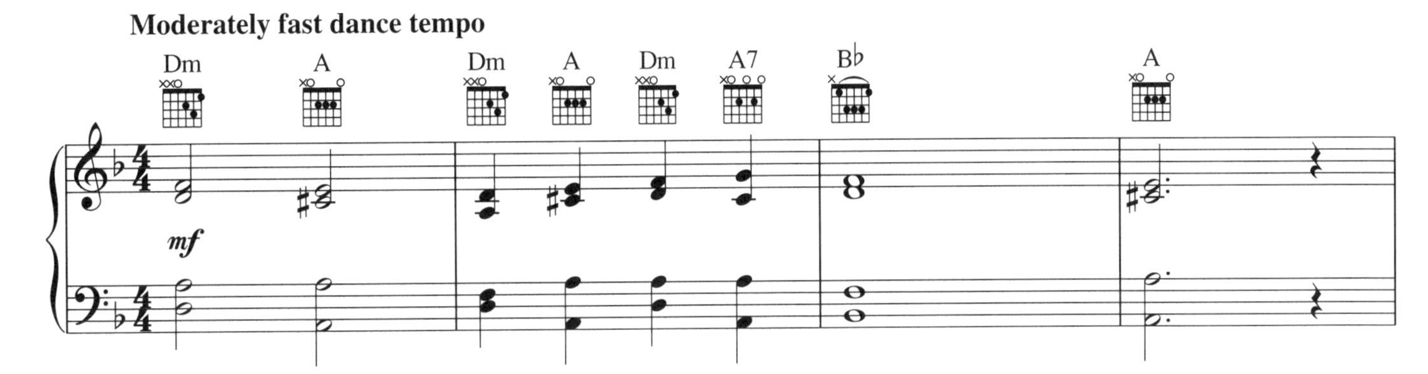

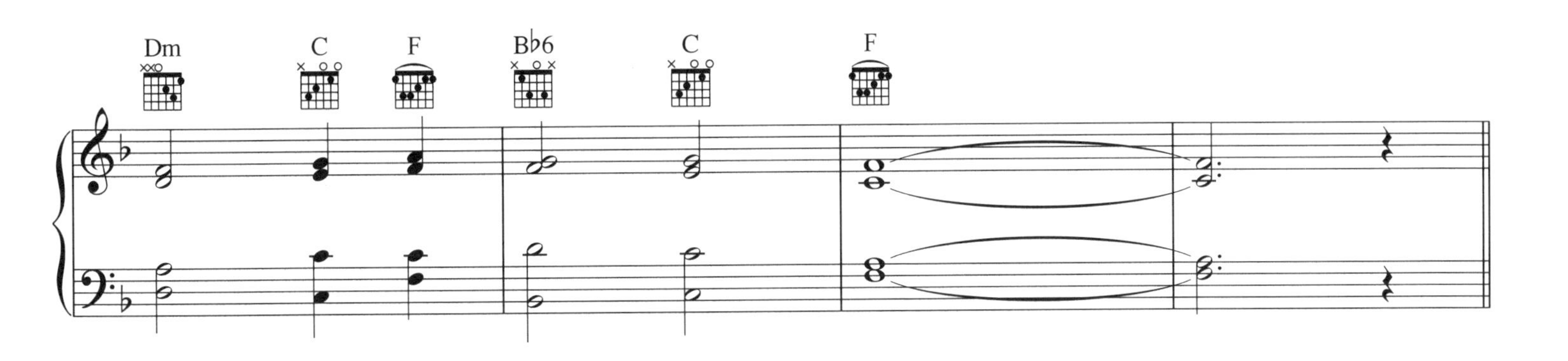

C
now ev - 'ry wom - an I see is a po - ten - tial threat,
a lit - tle small - talk, a smile and, ba - by, I was stuck.
they did - n't last ver - y long and they've been pret - ty scarce.
Dm
and I'm pos - ses - sive, it is - n't nice.
I still don't know what you've done with me,
I used to think that was sen - si - ble,
C
You've heard me say - ing that smok - ing was my on - ly vice.
a grown - up wom - an should nev - er fall so eas - i - ly.
it makes the truth e - ven more in - com - pre - hen - si - ble.
Dm
But now it is - n't true,
I feel a kind of fear
'Cause ev - 'ry - thing is new,
now
when
and

A7/C♯
Dm
ev - 'ry - thing is new and all I've learned has
I don't have you near, un - sat - is - fied I
ev - 'ry - thing is you, and all I've learned has
Edim7
Dm/F
G
o - ver - turned. I beg of you:
skip my pride. I beg you, dear:
o - ver - turned. What can I do?
Dm
A
Dm
A
Dm
A7
Don't go wast - ing your e -
B♭
A
Dm
C
F
mo - tion, lay all your

B♭6
C
F
To Coda
love
on
me.
1
Dm
2
Dm
A
Don't
go
Dm
A
Dm
A7
B♭
A
shar - ing
your
de - vo - tion,
Dm
C
F
B♭6
C
F
lay
all
your
love
on
me.

Dm
D.S. al Coda
CODA
Dm
A
Dm
A
Dm
A7
Don't go shar - ing your de -
Don't go wast - ing your e -
B♭
A
Dm
C
F
vo - tion,
mo - tion,
lay all your
B♭6
C
F
Repeat and Fade
love on me.

OUR LAST SUMMER

Words and Music by BENNY ANDERSSON
and BJÖRN ULVAEUS

Em Asus A
We had our chance, it was a fine and true ro - mance. I can still re -
D F♯m G A D F♯m
call our last sum - mer, I still see it all,
call our last sum - mer, I still see it all,
Gmaj7 A D F♯7 Bm Dmaj7/A
walks a - long the Seine, laugh - ing in the rain, our last
in the tour - ist jam 'round the No - tre Dame, our last
To Coda
G A Dsus D D/C♯
sum - mer, mem - 'ries that re - main. We made our way a - long the
sum - mer, walk - ing hand in

Bm7 D/A G D/F♯ Em Em/D
riv - er and we sat down in the grass by the Eif - fel Tow - er.
A E/G♯ Esus/F♯ E A A/G D/F♯ A7/E
I was so hap - py we had met, it was the age of no re - gret, oh
D D/C♯ Bm7 D/A G D/F♯ G6 A
yes. Those cra - zy years, that was the time of the flow - er - pow - er,
Em
but un - der - neath we had a fear of fly - ing, of get - ting old, a fear of slow - ly dy - ing.

Asus
A
D.S. al Coda
We took the chance like we were danc-ing our last dance. I can still re -
CODA
Dsus
A
D
F♯m
G
A
hand, Par - is res - tau - rants, our last sum - mer, morn-ing cro - is -
D
F♯m
Gmaj7
A
D
F♯7
sants, liv - ing for the day, wor - ries far a -
Bm
Dmaj7/A
G
A
Dsus
way, our last sum - mer, we could laugh and play.

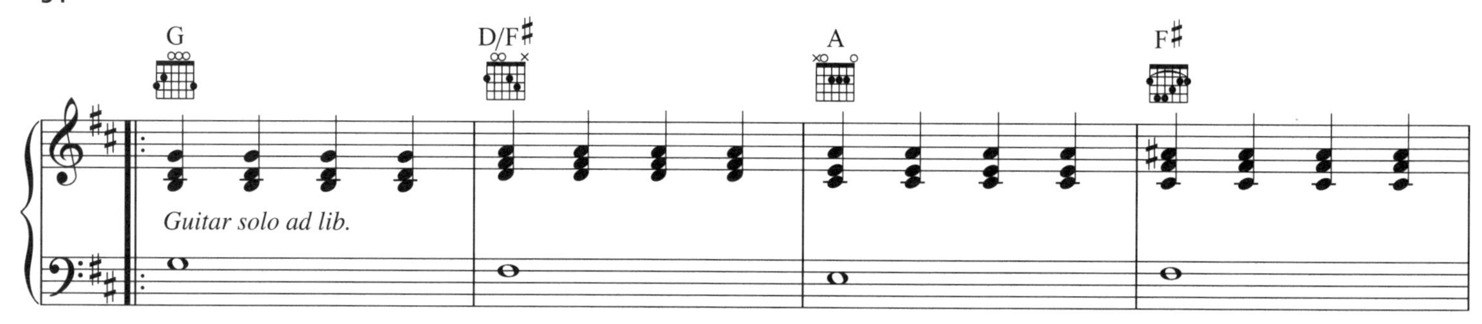
G
D/F♯
A
F♯
Guitar solo ad lib.

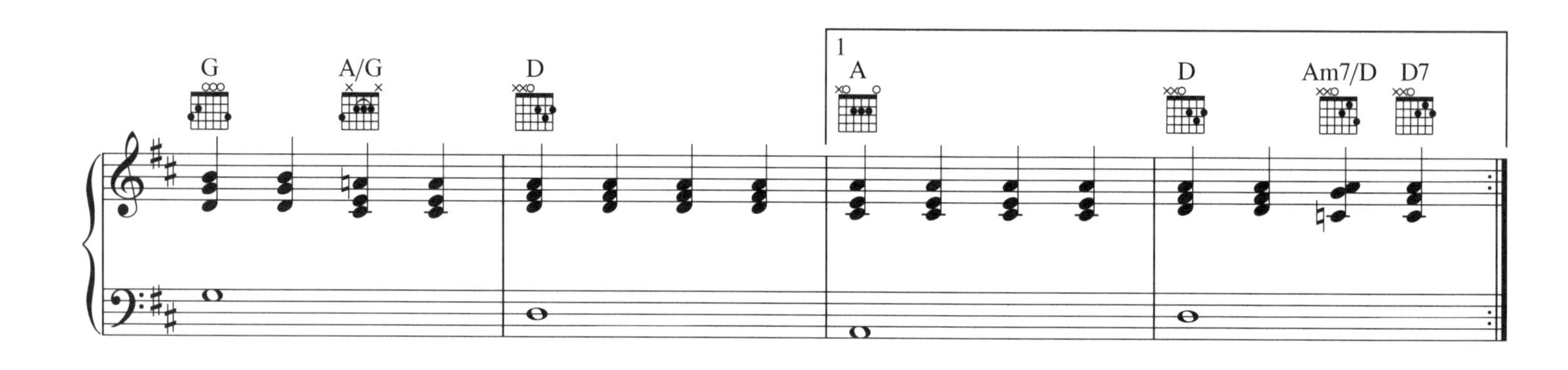
1
G
A/G
D
A
D
Am7/D
D7

2
Asus
D
D/C♯
Bm7
D/A
Solo ends
And now you're work- in' in a bank, a fam-'ly man, a foot-ball

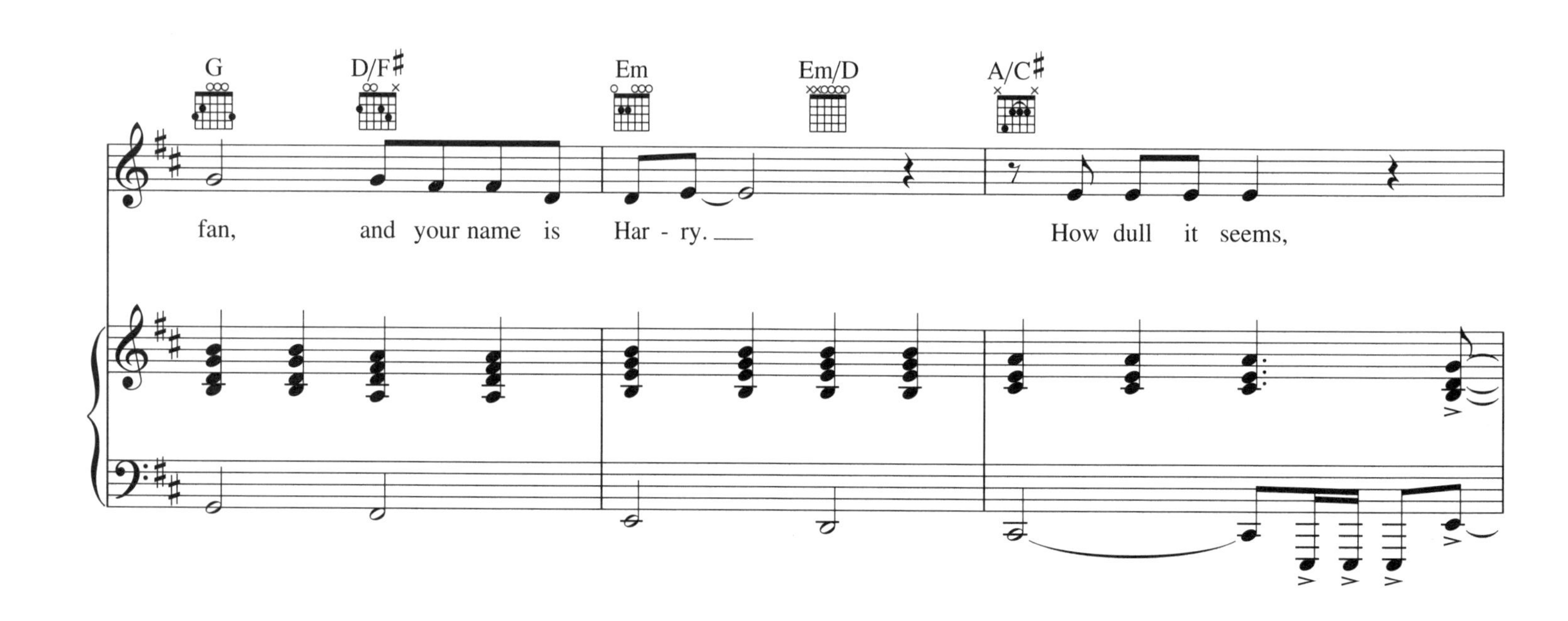
G
D/F♯
Em
Em/D
A/C♯
fan, and your name is Har - ry.
How dull it seems,

Em7
A
yet you're the he - ro of my dreams.
I can still re -
D
F#m
G
A
D
F#m
call our last sum - mer, I still see it all,
call our last sum - mer, I still see it all,
Gmaj7
A
D
F#7
Bm
Dmaj7/A
walks a - long the Seine, laugh - ing in the rain, our last
in the tour - ist jam 'round the No - tre Dame, our last
G
A
Dsus
A
Repeat ad lib. and Fade
sum - mer, mem - 'ries that re - main.
sum - mer, walk - ing hand in hand.
I can still re -
I can still re -

SUPER TROUPER

Words and Music by BENNY ANDERSSON
and BJÖRN ULVAEUS

C
Em7
Dm
I was sick and tired of ev - 'ry - thing when I called you last night from
Fac - ing twen - ty thou - sand of your friends, how can an - y - one be so
G6
G7
C
Em
Glas - gow. All I do is eat and sleep and sing wish - ing ev -
lone - ly. Part of a suc - cess that nev - er ends, still I'm think -
Dm
G6
G
F
- 'ry show was the last show. So i - mag - ine I was
- ing a - bout you on - ly. There are mo - ments when I
C/E
F
C/E
glad to hear you're com - ing, sud - den - ly I feel al - right,
think I'm go - ing cra - zy but it's gon - na be al - right,

F C/E Gsus

and it's gon - na be so dif - f'rent when I'm on the stage to - night.
ev - 'ry - thing will be so dif - f'rent when I'm on the stage to - night.

G G7 C Csus C

To - night the Su - per Trou - per lights are gon - na find me,

Csus C G7 Dm7

shin - ing like the sun, smil - ing, hav - ing

G C G7

fun, feel - ing like a num - ber one. To - night the

C
Csus
3fr
C
Csus
3fr
C
Su - per Trou - per beams are gon - na blind me but I won't feel
G7
Dm7
G
To Coda
blue like I al - ways do, 'cause
1
C
G7
some - where in the crowd there's you.
2
C
G7
C
some-where in the crowd there's you. So I'll be

F
Am
Dm
G
there when you ar - rive, the sight of you will prove to me I'm still a -
C
G
F
Dm
A7
live. And when you take me in your arms and hold me tight, I
Dm
G
G7
D.S. al Coda
know it's gon - na mean so much to - night. To - night the
CODA
G
C
some - where in the crowd there's you.

GIMME! GIMME! GIMME!
(A Man After Midnight)

Words and Music by BENNY ANDERSSON
and BJÖRN ULVAEUS

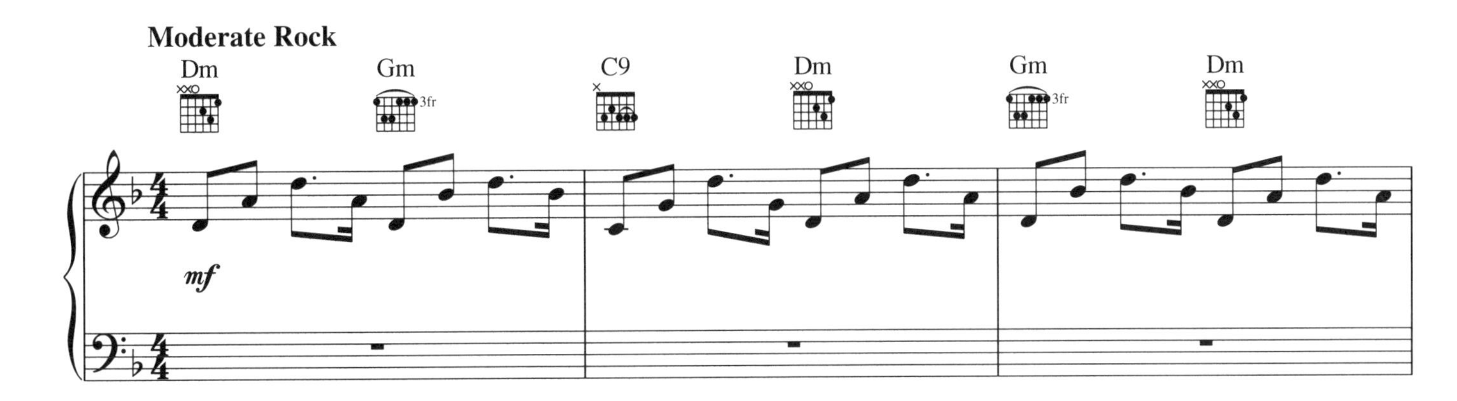

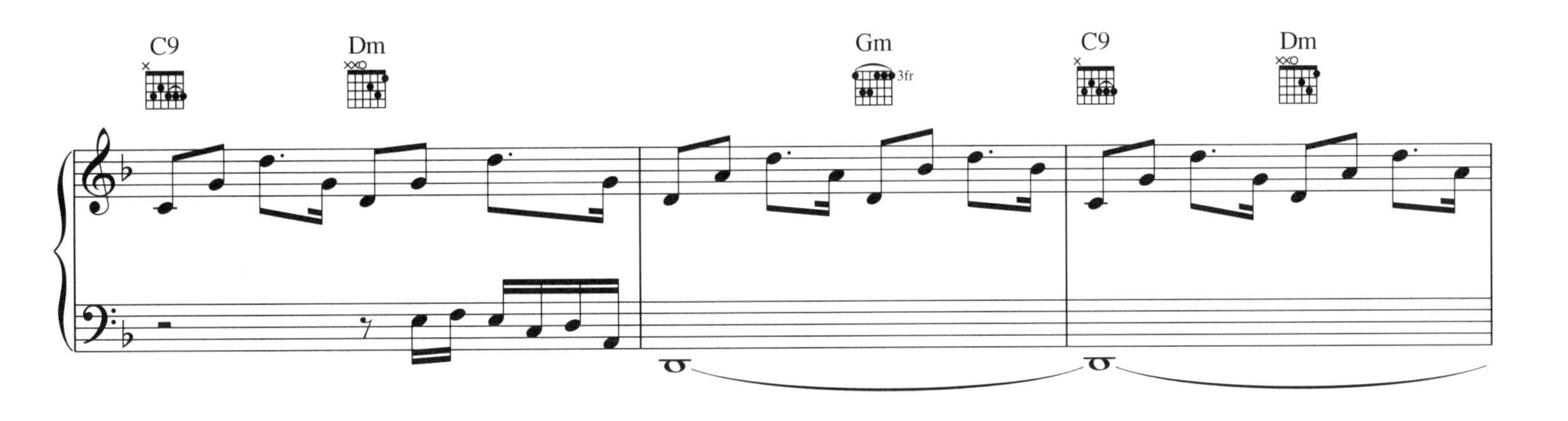

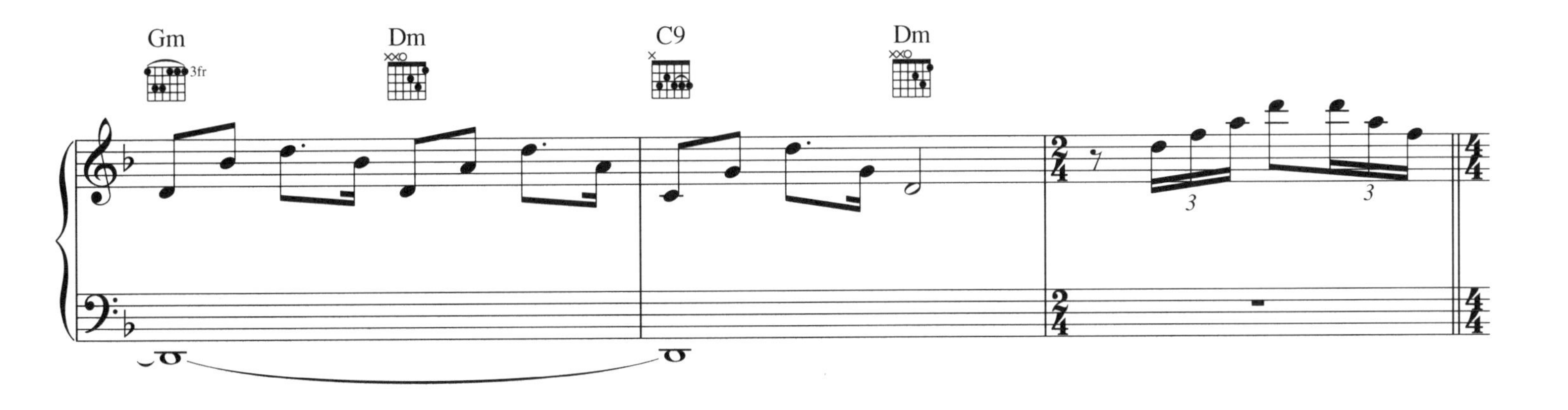

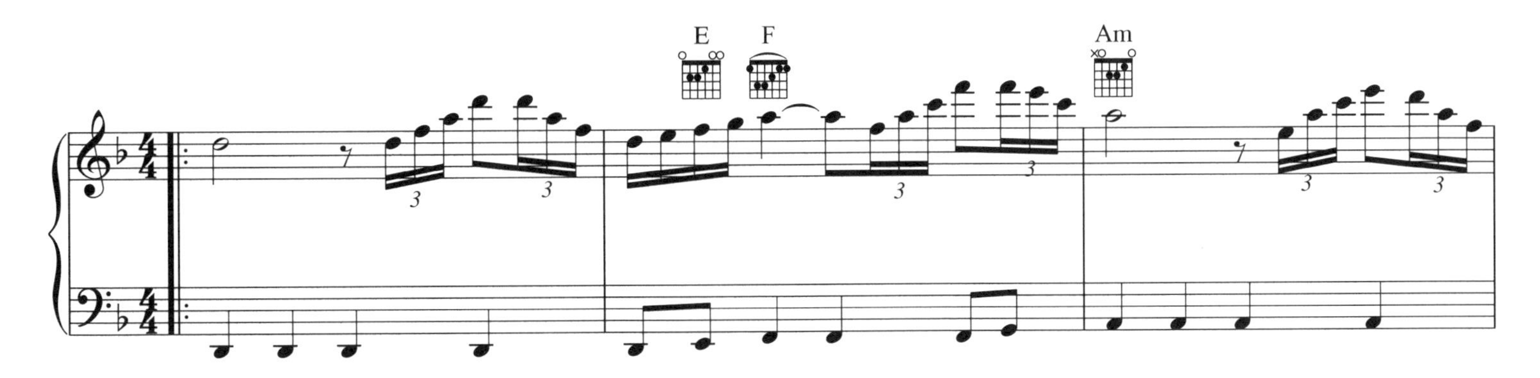

Dm
E
F

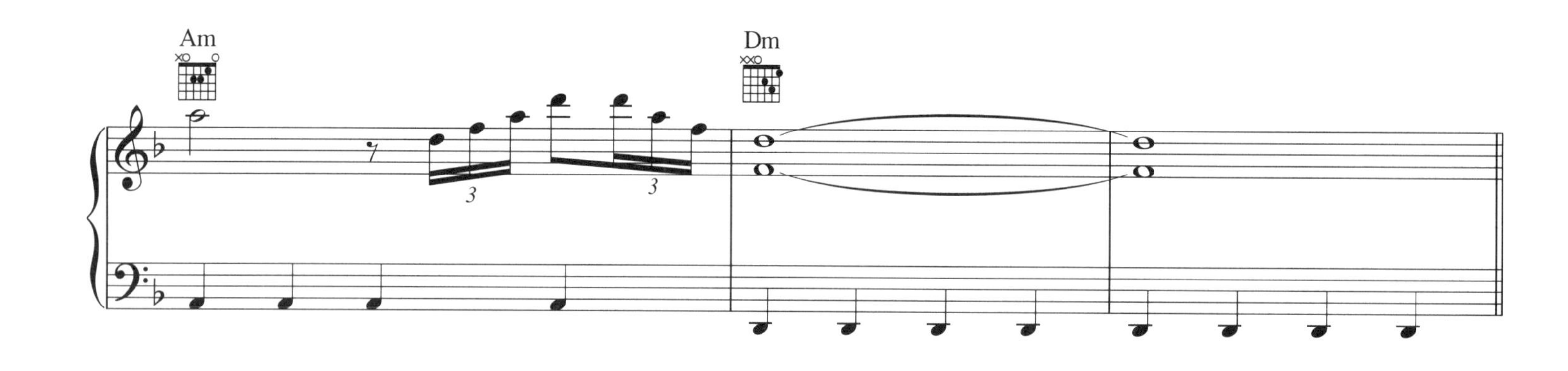
Am
Dm

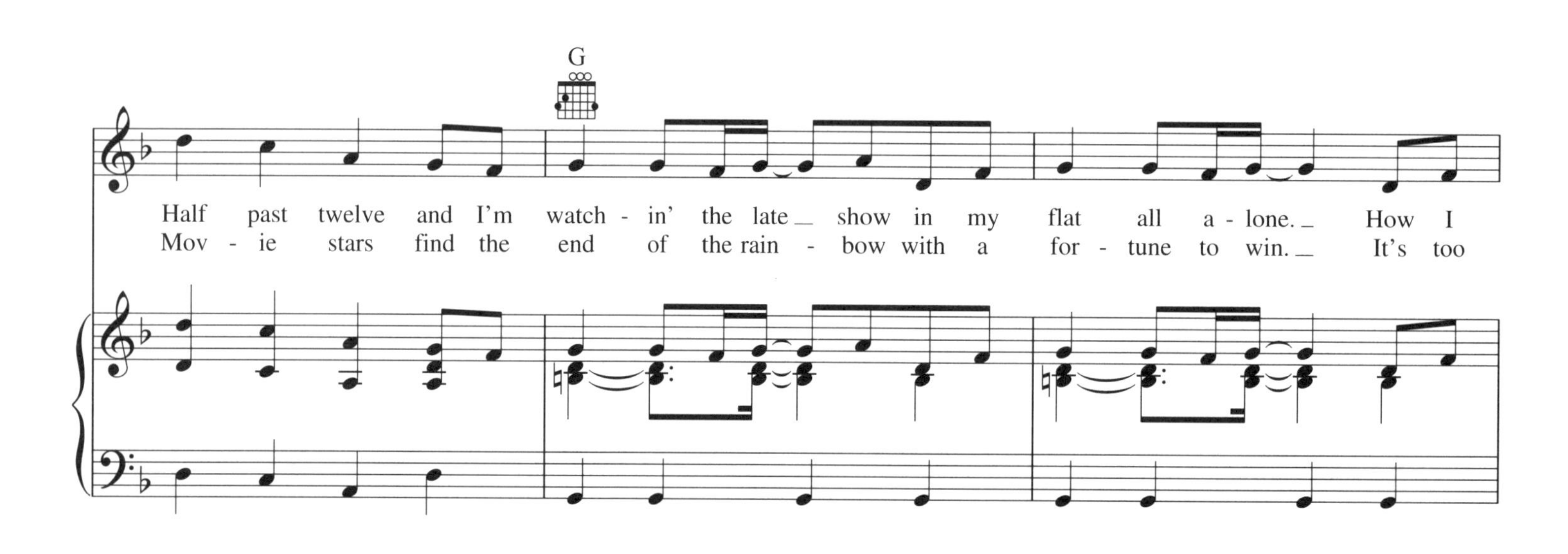
G
Half past twelve and I'm watch - in' the late _ show in my flat all a - lone. _ How I
Mov - ie stars find the end of the rain - bow with a for - tune to win. _ It's too

Dm
hate to spend the eve - ning on my own. Au - tumn winds blow - in'
dif - ferent from the world _ I'm liv - in' in. Tired of T - V I

G
out - side my win - dow as I look a - round the room and it
o - pen the win - dow and I gaze in - to the night, but there's
Dm
makes me so de - pressed to see the gloom.
noth - ing there to see, no one in sight.
B♭
There's not a soul out there,
Gm6
3fr
no one to hear my prayer.
Dm/A
A

Dm
Gm/B♭
C
Dm
Gm/B♭
Dm
Gim-me! Gim-me! Gim-me! a man after mid-night. Won't some-bod-y help me chase the
C
Dm
Gm/B♭
C
Dm
shad-ows a-way?
Gim-me! Gim-me! Gim-me! a man after mid-night. Won't
Gm/B♭
Dm
1
C
Dm
some-bod-y help me chase the shad-ows a-way?
3
3
2
C
Dm
Dm
Gm/B♭
C
Dm
shad-ows a-way?
Gim-me! Gim-me! Gim-me! a man after mid-night. Won't

Gm/B♭
Dm
C
Dm
Gm/B♭
some-bod-y help me chase the shad-ows a-way.
Gim-me! Gim-me! Gim-me! a man
C
Dm
Gm/B♭
Dm
C
Dm
af-ter mid-night, take me through the dark-ness to the break of the day.
E
F
Am
Dm
E
F
Am
Dm
Repeat and Fade

THE NAME OF THE GAME

Words and Music by BENNY ANDERSSON,
BJÖRN ULVAEUS and STIG ANDERSON

Dm
Am
Dm
Am
F♯m
C♯m
F♯m
C♯m
It seems to me for ev - 'ry time
Now I am here, talk - ing to you.
Dm
Am
Dm
G
F♯m
C♯m
F♯m
B
I'm get - ting more o - pen - heart - ed.
No won - der I get ex - cit - ed.
Dm
G/B
Am
B♭maj7
F♯m
B/D♯
C♯m
Dmaj7
I was an im - pos - si - ble case, no one ev - er could reach me,
Your smile and the sound of your voice, and the way you see through me,
Dm
G/B
Am
B♭maj7
F♯m
B/D♯
C♯m
Dmaj7
but I think I can see in your face there's a lot you can teach me.
got a feel - ing you gim - me no choice, but it means a lot to me.

Gm7
C11
F
Bm7
E11
A
So I wan - na know, what's the name of the game?
B♭maj7
C
C/B♭
F
B♭
Dmaj7
E
E/D
A
D
Does it mean an - y - thing to you?
C
B♭
F
B♭
E
D
A
D
What's the name of the game? Can you
C
C/B♭
F
A
E
E/D
A
C♯
feel it the way I do? Tell me, please,

Dm G/B C A
F♯m B/D♯ E C♯
'cuz I have to know. I'm a bash - ful child
Dm G/B C11
F♯m B/D♯ E11
be - gin - ning to grow. And you
F B♭/F
A D/A
make me talk, and you make me feel, and you
F B♭ E♭/B♭ B♭
A D G/D D
make me show what I'm try - ing to con - ceal. If I
6fr

F
B♭/F
A
D/A
trust in you,
would you let me down,
would you
F
Dm
A
F♯m
laugh at me?
If I said I care for you,
Em7
A7
B♭maj7
G♯m7
C♯7
Dmaj7
could you feel the same way, too? I
1
Gm7
C11
Dm7
Am
Bm7
E11
F♯m7
C♯m
wan-na know
the name of the game.

Dm
Am
Dm
Am
F♯m
C♯m
F♯m
C♯m
Dm
G
F♯m
B
2
Gm
C11
3fr
Bm
E11
wan - na know,
Gm
C11
3fr
Bm
E11
oh yes, I wan - na know the name of the game.
F
B♭
C
A
D
E
(I was an im - pos - si - ble case.) Does it mean an - y - thing

C/B♭
F
B♭
E/D
A
D
to you? (But I think I can see in your face,
C
B♭
F
E
D
A
and it means that I love you.) What's the name of the game?
(Your smile and the
B♭
C
C/B♭
F
D
E
E/D
A
sound of your voice.) Can you feel it the way I do? (Got a feel - ing you
B♭
C
B♭
D
E
D
Repeat and Fade
give me no choice, but it means that I love you.) What's the name of the game?

SOS

Words and Music by BENNY ANDERSSON,
BJÖRN ULVAEUS and STIG ANDERSON

F
C
Gm
3fr
What-ev-er hap-pened to our love?
I real-ly tried to make it out.
I wish I un-der-stood.
I wish I un-der-stood.
Dm
A7sus
A
It used to be so nice. It used to be so good.
What hap-pened to our love? It used to be so good.
Dm
A/C♯
Dm
Edim
F
Gm7
F
C7/E
F
C
Gm
B♭
F
B♭/F
So when you're near me, dar-ling, can't you hear me S. O. S.?

F
B♭/F
F
C
Gm
3fr
B♭
The love you gave me, noth - ing else can save me, S.
O. S.
When you're gone, how can I
D♭
E♭
e - ven try to go on?
When you're gone, though I try,

D♭
E♭
3fr
To Coda
1
F
how can I car - ry on?
2
F
A7♭9
5fr
F
A7♭9
5fr
Dm
A7/E
F
C7
D.S. al Coda

CODA
F
When you're gone,
B♭
D♭
E♭
3fr
F
how can I even try to go on?
B♭
D♭
E♭
3fr
When you're gone, though I try, how can I car - ry on?
F
A/E
Dm
rit.

VOULEZ-VOUS

Words and Music by BENNY ANDERSSON
and BJÖRN ULVAEUS

Disco

C

mf

R.H.

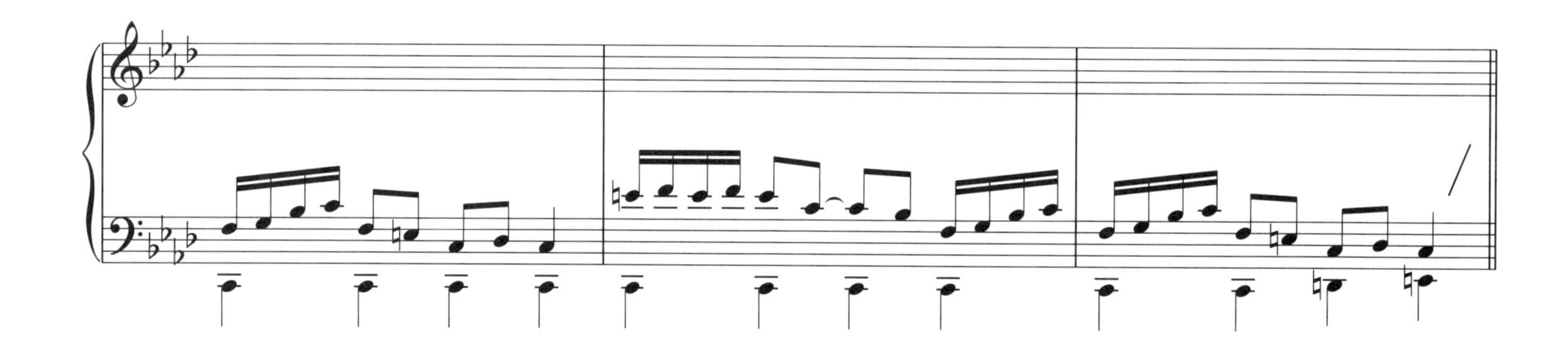

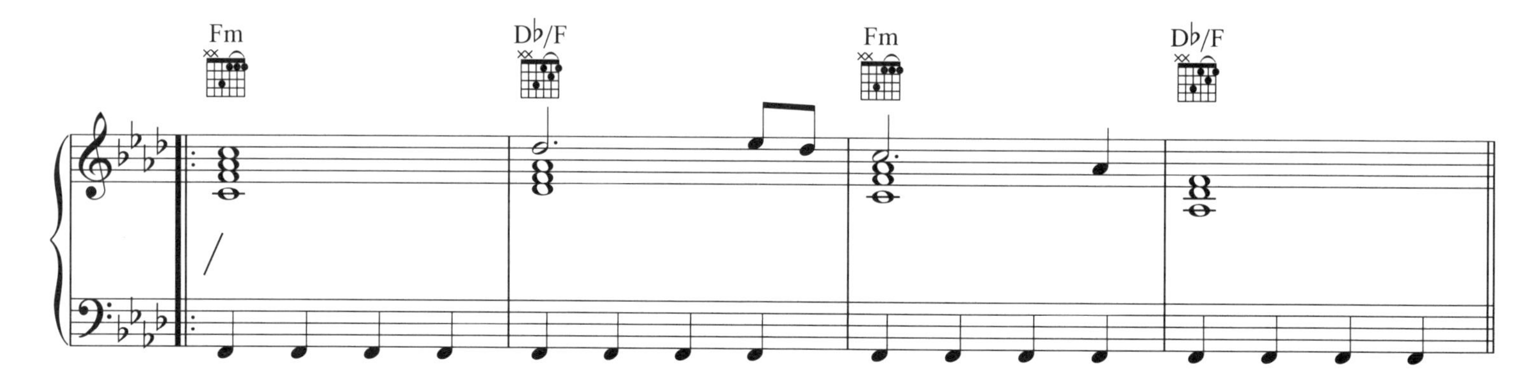

Fm
D♭/F
Peo - ple ev - 'ry - where, a sense of ex - pec - ta - tion
I know what you think; the girl means busi - ness so I'll
Fm
D♭/F
Fm
hang - in' in the air, giv - in' out a spark,
of - fer her a drink. Look - in' might - y proud,
D♭/F
Fm
D♭/F
Fm
a - cross the room your eyes are glow - in' in the dark. And here we
I see you leave your ta - ble push - in' through the crowd. I'm real - ly
C
(1., D.S.) go a - gain, we know the start, we know the end,
(2.) glad you came, you know the rules, you know the game,

Fm
C
mas - ters of the scene. We've done it
mas - ters of the scene. We've done it
all be - fore and now we're back to get some more,
all be - fore and now we're back to get some more,
Fm
D♭
B♭m
you know what I mean.
you know what I mean.
Vou - lez vous,
take it now or leave it, now is all we get,

Fm
D♭
nothing promised, no regrets.
Voulez
B♭m
vous,
ain't no big decision,
you know what to do,
la question c'est voulez
Fm
vous,
1, 3
D♭
B♭
C
voulez vous.
R.H.

To Coda
2
Fm
D.S. al Coda
(take lyric 1 and 1st ending)
And here we
CODA
Fm
D♭
Vou - lez
B♭m
vous, a - ha, a - ha, a - ha.

Fm
Db
Bbm
Vou - lez vous,
take it now or leave it, now is all we get,
ain't no big de - ci - sion, you know what to do,
noth - ing prom - ised, no re - grets.
la ques - tion c'est vou - lez vous.
Fm
Repeat and Fade
Optional Ending
Db
Bbm
Vou - lez vous.

DOES YOUR MOTHER KNOW

Words and Music by BENNY ANDERSSON
and BJÖRN ULVAEUS

Em
G
You're so hot teas - ing me. So you're blue,
I can see what you want but you seem
C
G/B
Am
G
D
but I can't take a chance on a chick like you.
pret - ty young to be search - ing for that kind of fun,
G
It's some - thing I could - n't do.
so may - be I'm not the one.
Em
G
There's that look in your eyes. I can read
You're so cute, I like your style, and I know

C
G/B
Am
G
D
in your face that your feel - ings are driv - ing you wild,
ah,
what you mean when you give me a flash of that smile,
ah,

G
but girl, you're on - ly a child.
but girl, you're on - ly a child.
Well, I could

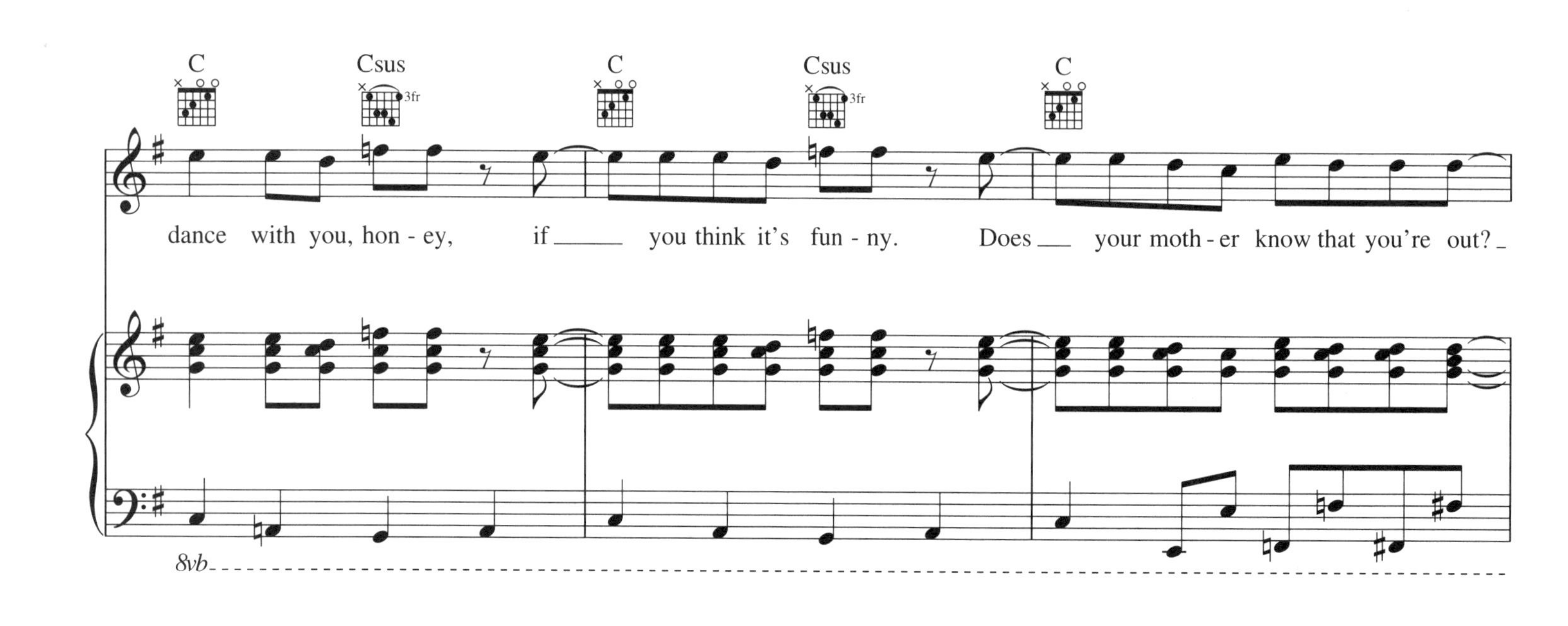
C
Csus
3fr
C
Csus
3fr
C
dance with you, hon - ey, if you think it's fun - ny. Does your moth - er know that you're out?
8vb

G
C
Csus
C
Csus
And I could chat with you, ba - by, flirt a lit - tle may - be. Does
(8vb)

C
G
your moth - er know that you're out? Take it eas - y, (take it eas - y,) bet - ter
(8vb)

C/G
Cm/G
G
Cm/G
G
Cm/G
3fr
slow down, girl. That's no way to go. (Does your moth - er know?) Take it

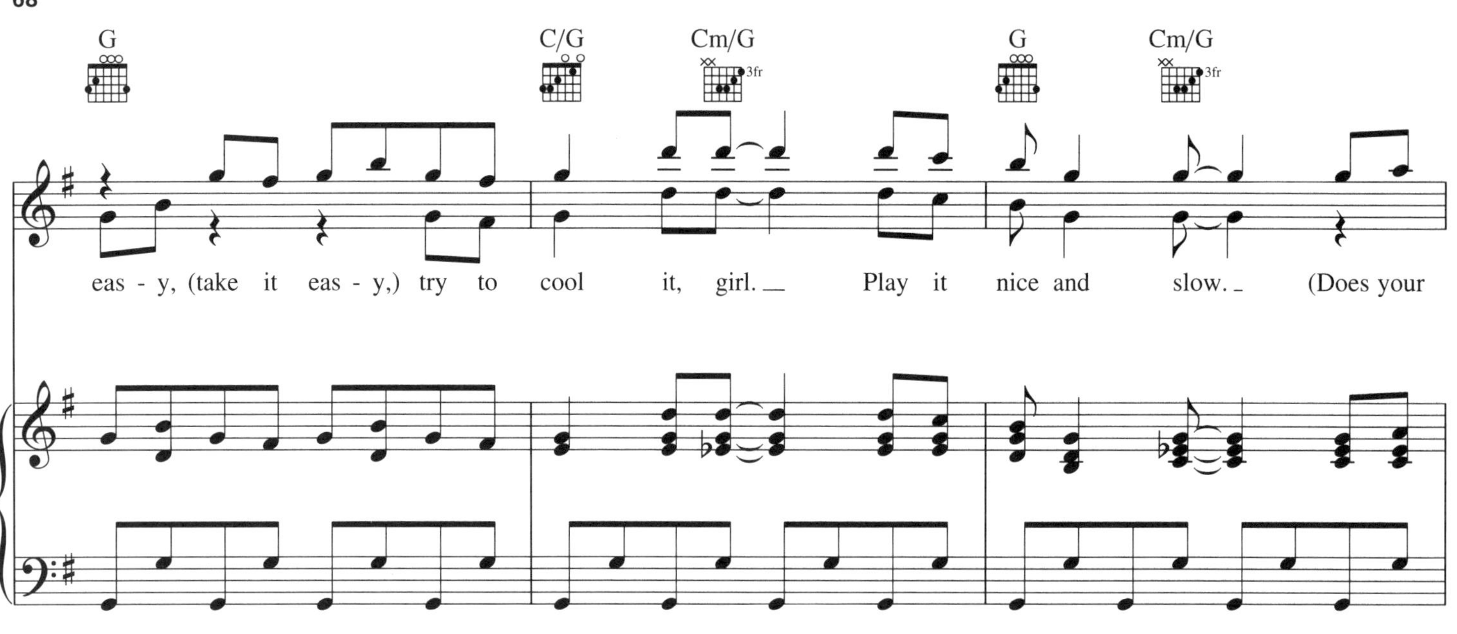
G
C/G
Cm/G
3fr
G
Cm/G
3fr
eas - y, (take it eas - y,) try to cool it, girl. Play it nice and slow. (Does your

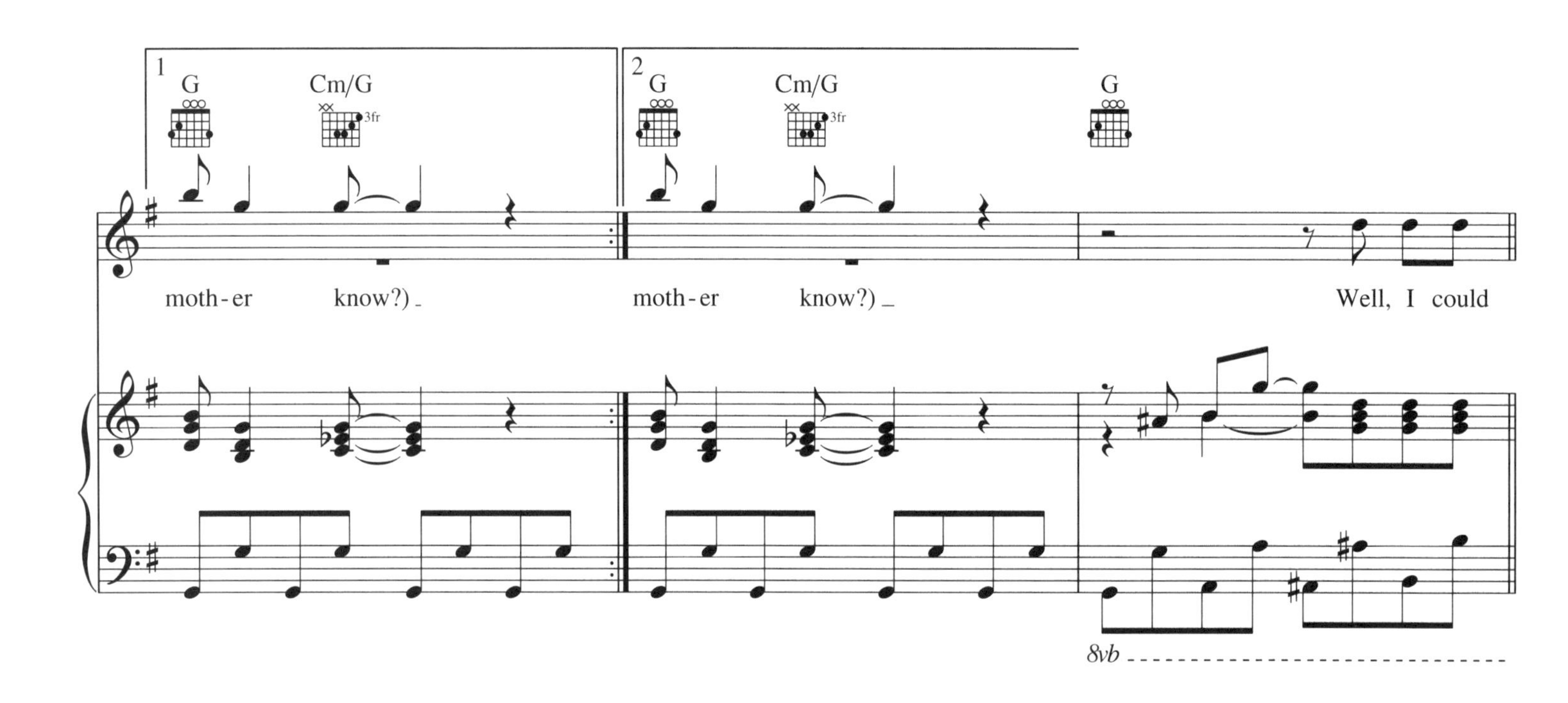
1
G
Cm/G
3fr
2
G
Cm/G
3fr
G
moth - er know?) moth - er know?) Well, I could
8vb

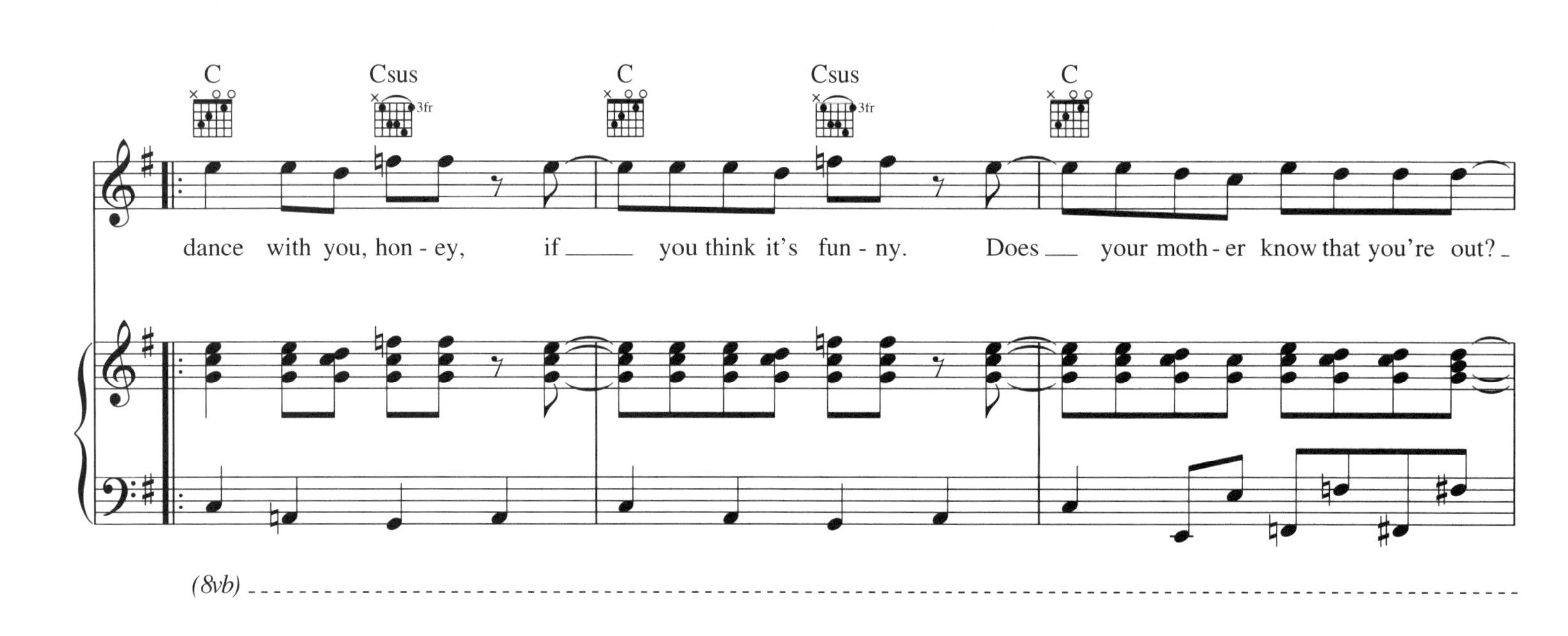
C
Csus
3fr
C
Csus
3fr
C
dance with you, hon - ey, if you think it's fun - ny. Does your moth - er know that you're out?
(8vb)

G
C
Csus
C
Csus
3fr
3fr
And I could chat with you, ba - by, flirt a lit - tle may - be. Does
(8vb)

Repeat and Fade
C
G
your moth - er know that you're out?
Well, I could
(8vb)

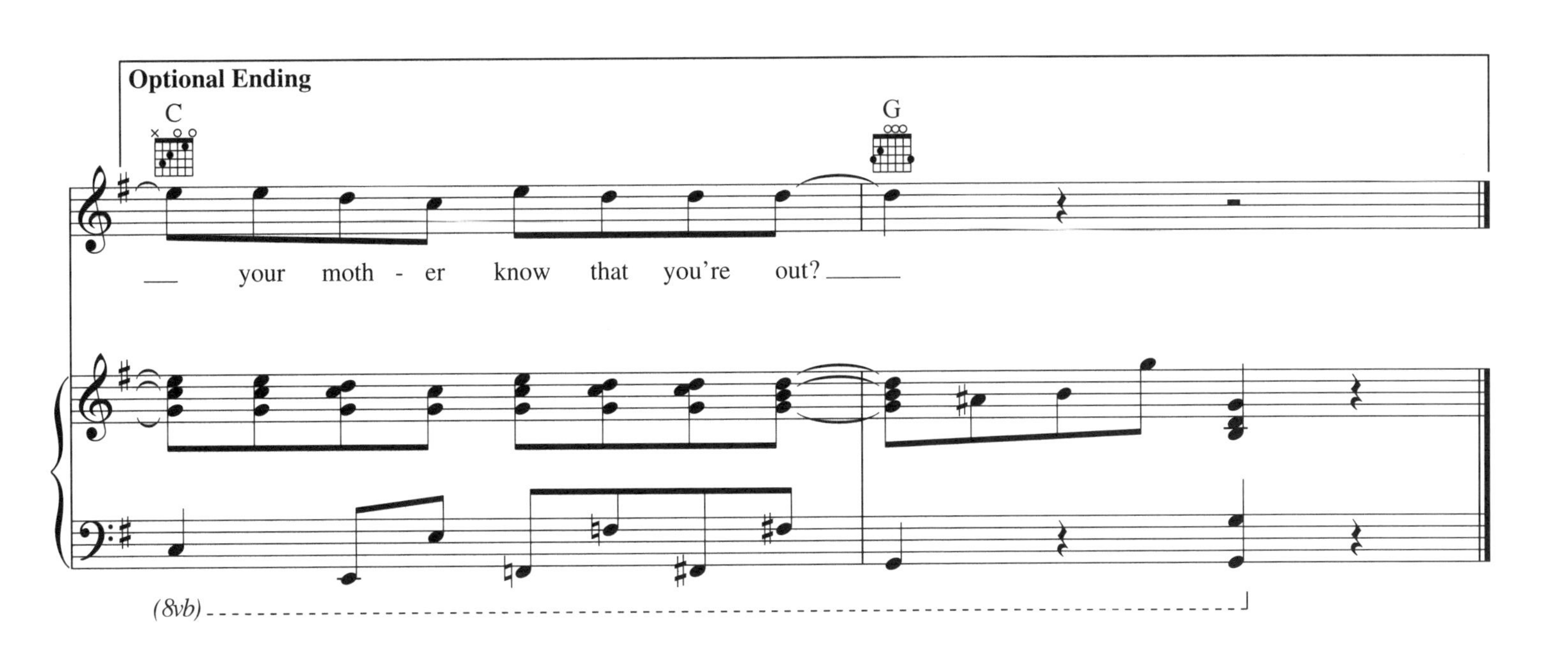
Optional Ending
C
G
your moth - er know that you're out?
(8vb)

SLIPPING THROUGH MY FINGERS

Words and Music by BENNY ANDERSSON
and BJÖRN ULVAEUS

B♭
Csus
C
F
and I have to sit down for a while. The
and a sense of guilt I can't de - ny. What
B♭
C/E
F
A+
A
feel - ing that I'm los - ing her for - ev - er and
hap - pened to the won - der - ful ad - ven - tures, the
B♭
C
F
with - out real - ly en - ter - ing her world. I'm
plac - es I had planned for us to go? Well,
B♭
C/E
F
Csus
C
glad when - ev - er I can share her laugh - ter, that fun - ny lit - tle girl.
some of that we did, but most we did - n't and why, I just don't know.

Fsus
F
B♭
F
Slip-ping through my fin-gers all the time, I try to cap-
Am
Gm
B♭
F
Csus
C
-ture ev-'ry min-ute, the feel-ing in it. Slip-ping through my fin-gers all the time,
F
B♭
F
do I real-ly see what's in her mind? Each time I think I'm close to know-
Gm
B♭
F
Csus
C
1
F
-ing she keeps on grow-ing. Slip-ping through my fin-gers all the time.

2
F
B♭
C
F
A+
A
Some - times I wish that I could freeze the pic - ture and
B♭
C
F
B♭
C
save it from the fun - ny tricks of time. Slip-ping through my fin - gers.
F
B♭
F
Am
Gm
3fr
B♭
F
Csus
3fr
C
F

B♭
F
Am
Gm
3fr
B♭
F
Csus
3fr
C
F
Slip-ping through my fin-gers all the time.
B♭/D
B♭m/D♭
F/C
Am
School - bag in hand, she leaves home in the ear - ly morn - ing,
mp
B♭/D
B♭m/D♭
F/C
Am
wav - ing good - bye with an ab - sent - mind - ed smile.
rit. e dim.

THE WINNER TAKES IT ALL

Words and Music by BENNY ANDERSSON
and BJÖRN ULVAEUS

A♭m/E♭
D♭
me, now it's his - to - ry.
sense, build - ing me a fence,
same when she calls your name?
stand you've come to shake my hand.
G♭
I've played all my cards and that's what you've
build - ing me a home, think - ing I'd be
Some - where deep in - side you must know I
I a - pol - o - gize if it makes you
D♭/F
A♭m/E♭
4fr
done, too, noth - ing more to say,
strong there, but I was a fool,
miss you, but what can I say,
feel bad see - ing me so tense,

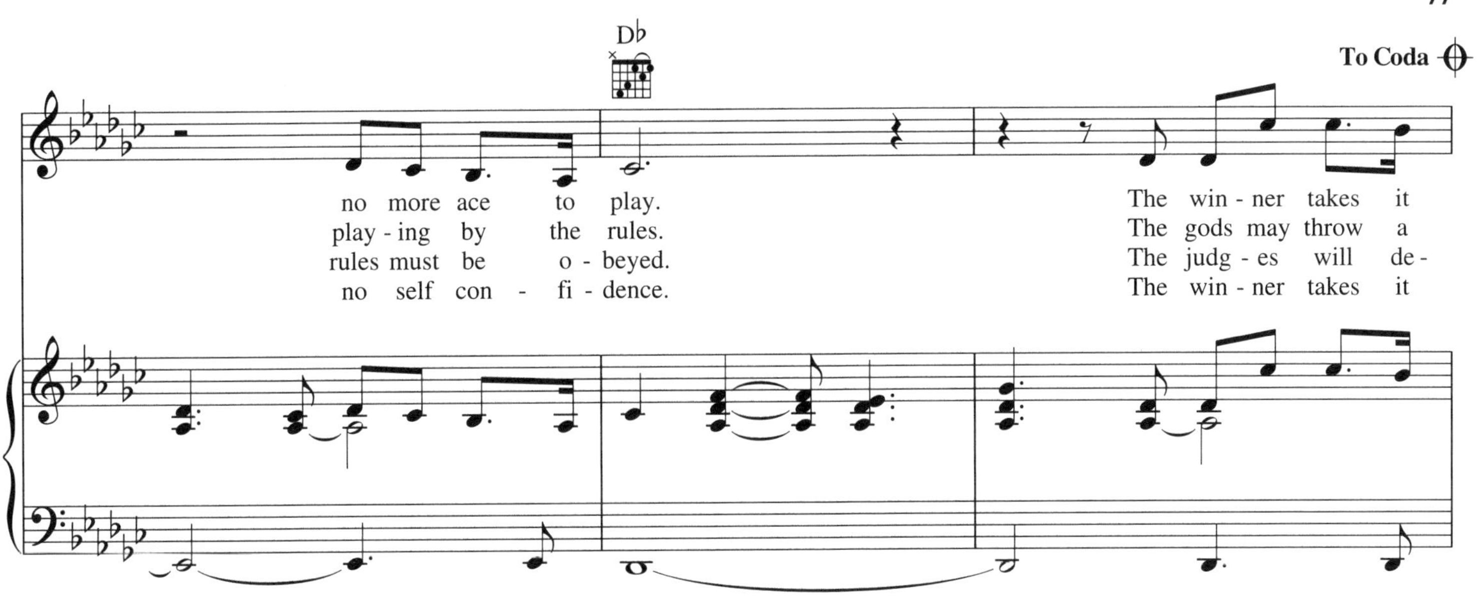
To Coda
D♭
no more ace to play.
play - ing by the rules.
rules must be o - beyed.
no self con - fi - dence.
The win - ner takes it
The gods may throw a
The judg - es will de -
The win - ner takes it

G♭
B♭7/D
E♭m
6fr
all,
dice,
cide,
the los - er stand - ing small
their minds as cold as ice,
the likes of me a - bide,

E♭7/G
A♭m
4fr
be - side the vic - to - ry,
and some - one way down here
spec - ta - tors of the show
that's her des - ti -
los - es some - one
al - ways stay - ing

D♭
1
2, 3
ny.
dear.
low.
I was in your
The win - ner takes it
The game is on a -
G♭
B♭7/D
E♭m
6fr
E♭7/G
all,
gain,
the los - er has to fall,
a lov - er or a friend,
it's sim - ple and it's
a big thing or a
A♭m
4fr
D♭
plain,
small,
why should I com - plain.
the win - ner takes it all.
1
2
D.S. al Coda
But tell me, does she
I don't wan - na

CODA
G♭
B♭7/D
E♭m
6fr
all.
E♭7/G
A♭m
4fr
D♭
The win - ner takes it all.
G♭
B♭7/D
E♭m
6fr
E♭7/G
A♭m
4fr
D♭
Repeat and Fade

WHEN ALL IS SAID AND DONE

Words and Music by BENNY ANDERSSON
and BJÖRN ULVAEUS

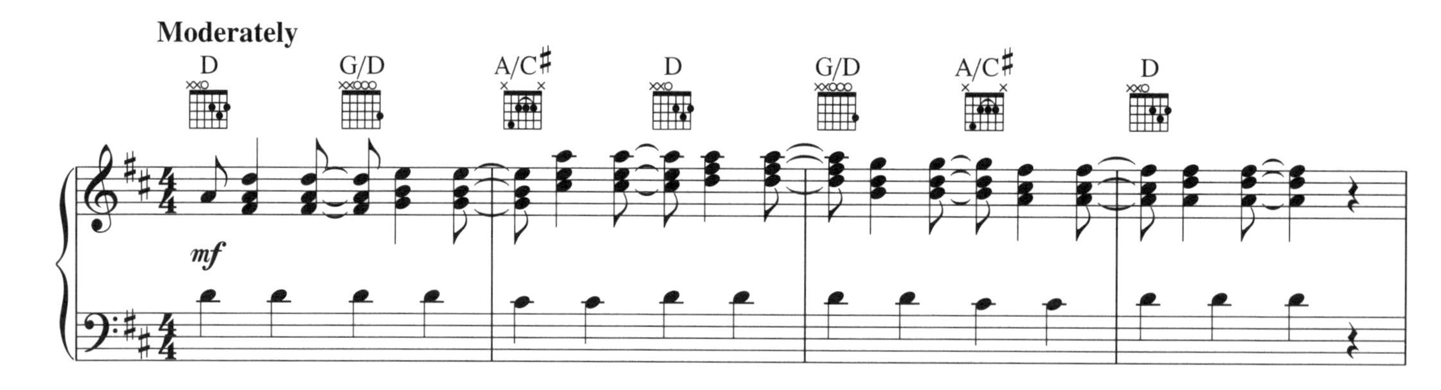

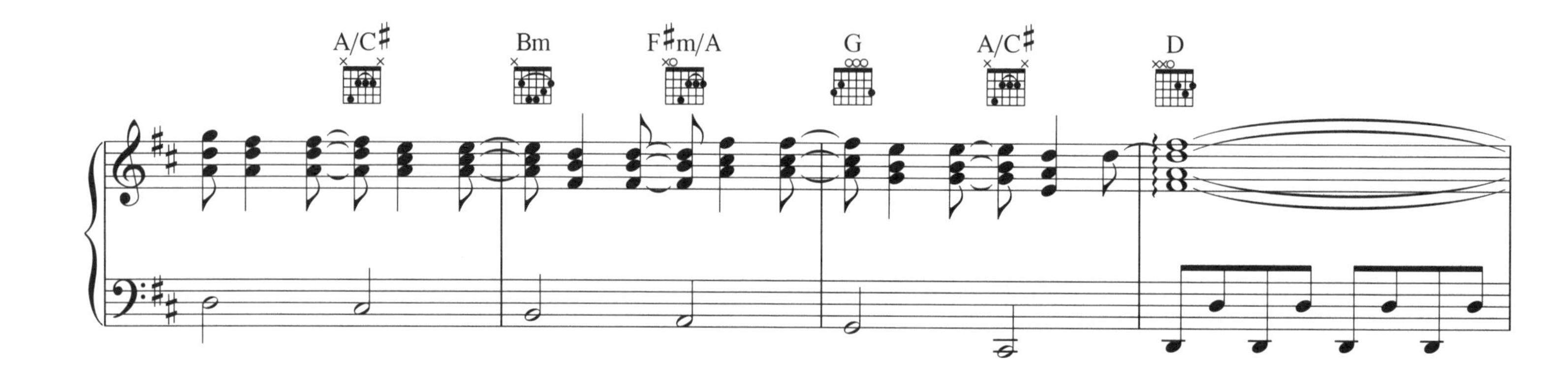

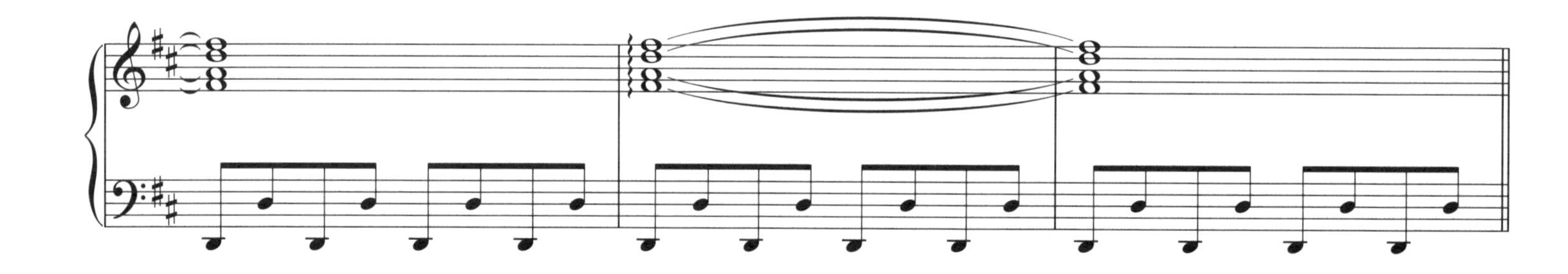

D
G
Deep in - side both of us can feel
slight-ly worn but dig-ni - fied and not
how you rise, shake your head, get up
A
D
G/D
the au - tumn chill.
too old for sex.
and ask for more.
Birds of pas - sage, you
We're still striv - ing for
Clear-head - ed and o -
A/D
D
G/D
A/D
D
and me, we fly in - stinc - tive - ly.
the sky, no taste for hum - ble pie.
- pen - eyed with noth - ing left un - tried.
A/C♯
Bm
F♯m/A
G
A7/C♯
When the sum - mer's o - ver and the dark clouds hide the sun,
Thanks for all your gen - 'rous love and thanks for all the fun.
Stand - ing calm - ly at the cross - roads, no de - sire to run.

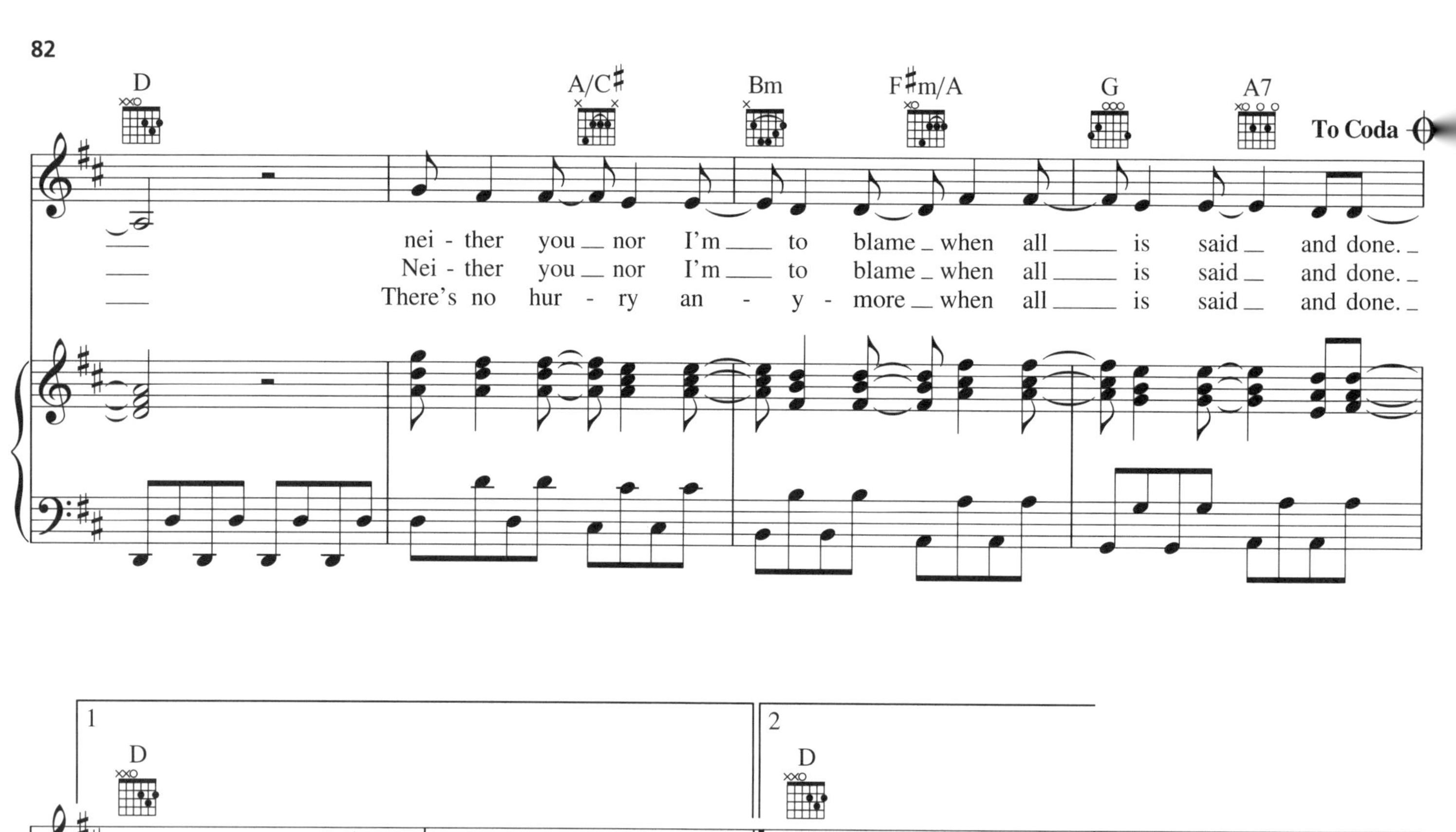
D
A/C♯
Bm
F♯m/A
G
A7
To Coda
nei - ther you _ nor I'm _ to blame _ when all _ is said _ and done. _
Nei - ther you _ nor I'm _ to blame _ when all _ is said _ and done. _
There's no hur - ry an - y - more _ when all _ is said _ and done. _

1
D
2
D

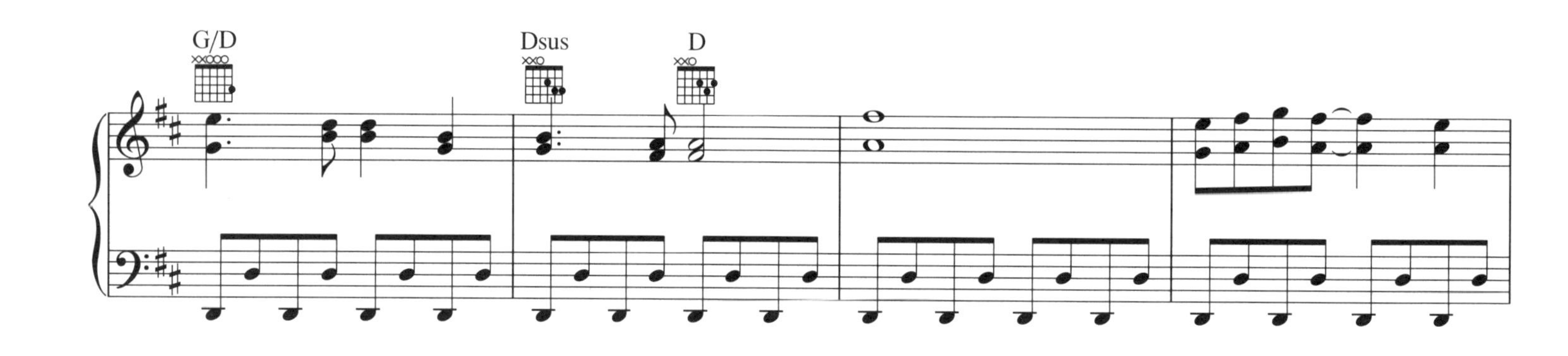
G/D
Dsus
D

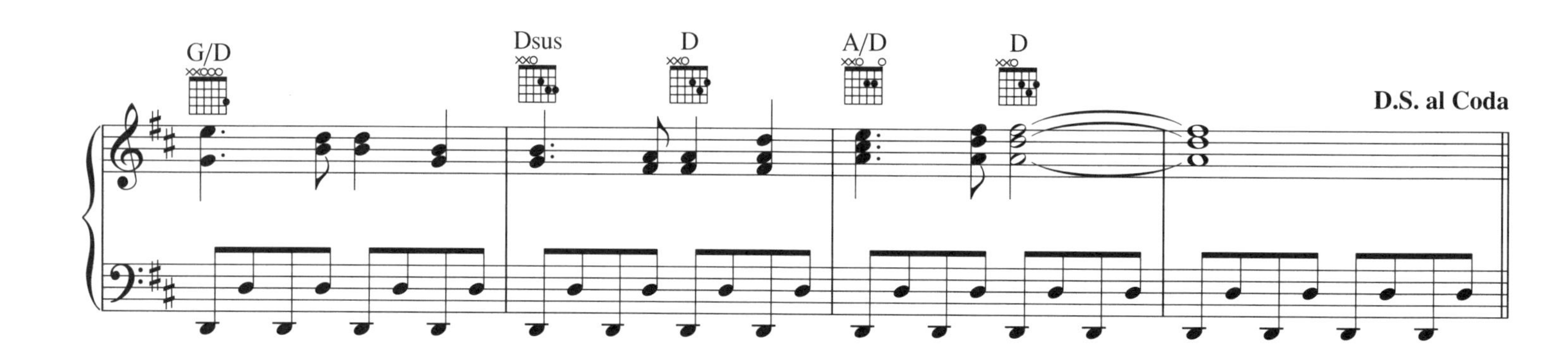
G/D
Dsus
D
A/D
D
D.S. al Coda

CODA
D
A/C♯
Bm
F♯m/A
G
A7/C♯
Stand-ing calm - ly at the cross - roads, no de - sire to run.
D
A/C♯
Bm
G
A7
There's no hur - ry an - y - more when all is said and done.
D
G/D
Dsus
D
Repeat and Fade
G/D
Dsus
D

TAKE A CHANCE ON ME

Words and Music by BENNY ANDERSSON
and BJÖRN ULVAEUS

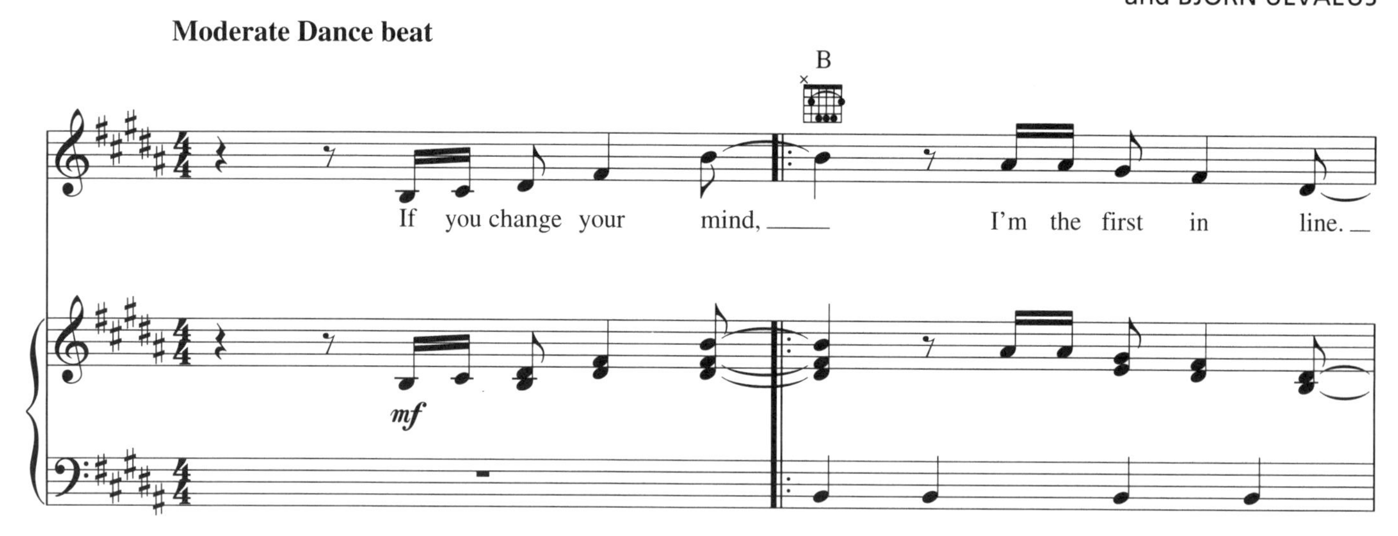

B
feel - ing down.
If you're all a - lone
when the pret - ty birds have flown, hon - ey, I'm still free,
take a chance on me.
F♯
Gon - na do my ver -
- y best, and it ain't no lie,
if you put me to the test, if you

B
C♯m
F♯
let me try. Take a chance on me, take a
C♯m
F♯
C♯m
chance on me.
We can go danc - ing,
Oh, you can take your time, ba - by,
B
we can go walk - ing as long as we're to - geth - er.
I'm in no hur - ry, I know I'm gon - na get you.
C♯m
Lis - ten to some mu - sic
You don't wan - na hurt me,

B
may - be just talk - ing, you'd get to know me bet - ter
ba - by, don't wor - ry I ain't gon - na let you.
G♯m
'cause you know I got so much that I wan - na do.
Let me tell you now my love is strong e - nough
E
G♯m
E
F♯
When I dream I'm a - lone with you, it's mag - ic.
to last when things are rough, it's mag - ic.
G♯m
E
You want me to leave it there, a - fraid of a love af - fair, but I
You say that I waste my time, but I can't get it off my mind. No, I

C♯m
F♯
C♯m
think you know
that I can't let go.
can't let go
'cause I love you so.
F♯
B
If you change your mind,
If you change your mind,
I'm the first in line.
Hon-ey, I'm still free,
F♯
take a chance on me.
If you need me, let
me know. Gon-na be a - round,
if you got no place to go when you're

B
feel - ing down. _
If you're all a - lone ___
when the pret - ty birds _
___ have flown, hon - ey, I'm still free, ___
take a chance on me. ___
F♯
___ Gon-na do my ver - y best, ba-by, can't you see, ___
got-ta put me to _
___ the test, take a chance on me. ___
B
Repeat and Fade
If you change your mind, _

I HAVE A DREAM

Words and Music by BENNY ANDERSSON
and BJÖRN ULVAEUS

B♭
F7
of a fair - y tale,
you can take the fu - ture
B♭
To Coda
F7
ev - en if you fail.
I be - lieve in an - gels,
E♭
3fr
B♭
F7
some - thing good in ev - 'ry - thing I see.
I be - lieve in an - gels
E♭
3fr
B♭
F7
when I know the time is right for me, I'll cross the stream,

B♭
F7
I have a dream.
I have a dream,
a fan - ta - sy,
to help me through
re - al - i - ty.
And my des - ti - na - tion
makes it worth the while,
push-ing through the dark - ness

B♭
still an-oth - er mile.
I be - lieve in
F7
E♭
3fr
B♭
an - gels,
some-thing good in ev - 'ry-thing I see.
I be-lieve in
F7
E♭
3fr
an - gels
when I know the time is right for
B♭
F7
B♭
me, I'll cross the stream,
I have a dream.

F7
B♭sus
I'll cross the stream,
I have a dream.
B♭
F7
B♭
B♭sus
B♭
F7
B♭
D.S. al Coda
I have a

CODA
B♭
F7
I be - lieve in an - gels,
E♭
3fr
B♭
some - thing good in ev - 'ry - thing I see. I be - lieve in
F7
E♭
3fr
an - gels when I know the time is right for
B♭
F7
me, I'll cross the stream, I have a

B♭
F7
dream.
I'll cross the stream,
I have a
B♭sus
B♭
dream. Na na na na na na na na na na na na na na na na na na na
2
4
F7
B♭
B♭sus
na, na na na na na. Na na na na na na na
F7
Repeat and Fade
na na na na na na na na na na na na na, na na na na na, na na na na,